PUFFIN BOOKS

CONDENSED ANIMA

No one looks at the animal
as Spike Milligan. Strange creatures and comic twists
abound in this witty and entertaining (and very silly)
collection of short, sharp poems that Milligan fans
everywhere will enjoy.

Spike Milligan is well known as a writer for both
children and adults. His other books of poems for
children include *Unspun Socks From a Chicken's
Laundry*, *Silly Verse for Kids* and *A Book of
Milliganimals*, but he has also written many books for
adults. He is an acclaimed comic and for many years
has appeared regularly on television and radio.

Other books by Spike Milligan

A Book of Milliganimals

Silly Verse for Kids

Startling Verse for all the Family

Unspun Socks From a Chicken's
   Laundry

Condensed Animals

Spike Milligan

Illustrated by
Kathryn Lamb

PUFFIN Books

For Hastie, Brodie and Jay

PUFFIN BOOKS

Published by the Penguin Group
Penguin Books Ltd, 27 Wrights Lane, London w8 5tz, England
Penguin Books USA Inc., 375 Hudson Street, New York, New York 10014, USA
Penguin Books Australia Ltd, Ringwood, Victoria, Australia
Penguin Books Canada Ltd, 10 Alcorn Avenue, Toronto, Canada m4v 3b2
Penguin Books (NZ) Ltd, 182–190 Wairau Road, Auckland 10, New Zealand

Penguin Books Ltd, Registered Offices: Harmondsworth, Middlesex, England

First published 1991
10 9 8 7 6 5 4 3 2 1

Text copyright © Spike Milligan Productions Limited, 1991
Illustrations copyright © Kathryn Lamb, 1991
All rights reserved

The moral right of the author has been asserted

Printed in England by Clays Ltd, St Ives plc
Filmset in 15/29 pt Monophoto Ehrhardt

Condensed animals was written for those adults and children who do not like long rambling poems. If you want a long rambling poem then just read the contents of this book at one go.

This is not a coffee-table book, rather it's an Ovaltine one.

Spike Milligan

Contents

Ant   1

Pouter pigeon   2

Mole   3

Bat   4

Toad   5

Skylark   6

Penguin   7

Horse   8

Gorilla   9

Mule   10

Stork   11

Glow-worm   12

Aardvark 13

Cow 14

Monkey 15

Eagle 16

Giraffe 17

Hyena 18

Pussy-cat 19

Hippopotamus 20

Elephant 21

Owl 22

Orang-utan 23

Snail 24

Frog 25

Bee 26

Flea 27

Bug 28

Fly 29

Butterfly 30

Grasshopper 31

Fish 32

Snake 33

Duck 34

Cockerel 35

Cricket 36

Elephant 37

Lamb 38

Chicken 39

Pig 40

Leopard 41

Tortoise 42

Gnu 43

Salmon 44

Termite 45

Porpoise 46

Sea-gull   47

Badger   48

Piranha   49

March hare   50

Whale   51

Moth   52

Dragon-fly   53

Whale   54

Wasp   55

Sea-lion   56

Zebra   57

Antelope   58

Tiger   59

Alligator   60

Hedgehog   61

Fox   62

Water-buffalo   63

Swallow 64

Sea snake 65

Kangaroo 66

Wart-hog 67

Crow 68

Chimpanzee 69

Toucan 70

Jellyfish 71

Seal 72

Ostrich 73

Turtle 74

Starfish 75

Sardine 76

Camel 77

Caterpillar 78

Skate 79

Rhinoceros 80

Highland deer   81

Centipede   82

Woodpecker   83

Tuna   84

Worm   85

Bluebottle   86

Cockroach   87

Polar bear   88

Polecat   89

Kinkajou   90

Lizard   91

Millipede   92

Cockatoo   93

Wolf   94

Sea-horse   95

Mongoose   96

Yak   97

Otter   98

Ostrich   99

Octopus   100

Reindeer   101

Pretty Polly   102

Budgerigar   103

Albatross   104

Gazelle   105

Boar   106

Lobster   107

Krill   108

Locust   109

Ant

Little ant – little ant

Working all the day

Don't you ever want to go

Go outside and play?

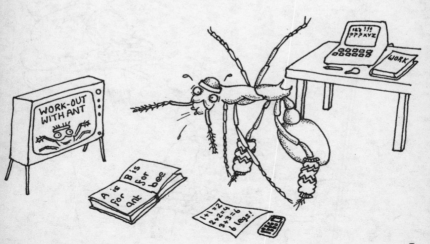

Pouter pigeon

Puffery pouter pigeon

With your puffed-up chest

If I did that

My mum would make me

Go and wear a vest.

Mole

Mr Mole – Mr Mole

Burrowing under the green

It's no wonder – it's no wonder

That you're very rarely seen.

Bat

Bat bat bat bat

Flying in the night

Said my mum

When she saw one

It gave her quite a fright.

4

Toad

Toad toad

Little toad

Be careful how

You cross the road.

WAIT FOR THE LITTLE GREEN TOAD, DEAR!

DO YOU KNOW YOUR HIGHWAY TOAD?

Skylark

Skylark skylark

Up high you sing your song

I want to know just how you stay

You stay up there so long.

Penguin

Penguin penguin

Sliding on the ice

Freezing your tootsies

Can't be very nice.

Horse

The horse of course
We like very much
Unless he kicks you
In the crutch.

Gorilla

Gorilla gorilla

I love gorillas

But not as Christmas

Stocking fillers.

Mule

He's half donkey

Half horse

He is in fact

A mule of course.

Stork

A stork will stand

On one leg all day

It's done to rest

The other they say.

Glow-worm

Glow-worm glow-worm

With your flashing light

Yet they say at school

You're not very bright!

Aardvark

Aardvark aardvark

Living in Bolivia

Where the jaguars eat you

Wouldn't you rather live in 'ere?

13

Cow

The cow will give

A gentle moo

But that and milk

Is all she'll do.

Monkey

Monkey monkey

Pulling faces

Round and round

And round he races.

Up and down

In and out

What is that monkey

All about?

15

Eagle

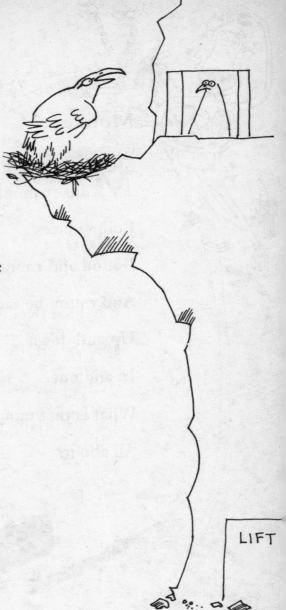

Eagle Eagle

In your eyrie

Flying up there

Must be weary.

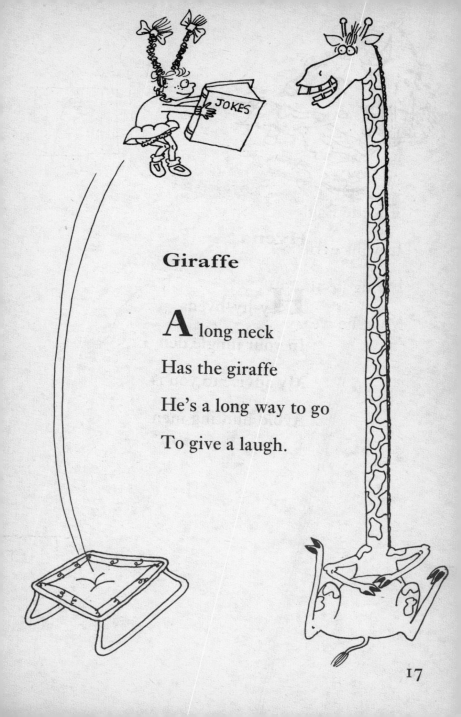

Giraffe

A long neck

Has the giraffe

He's a long way to go

To give a laugh.

17

Hyena

Hy-hy-hyena

In your jungle den

My advice to you is

Avoid hunting men.

Pussy-cat

Pussy-cat

What are vices?

Catching rats

And eating mices!

Hippopotamus

Hip-po hip-po

Hippopotamus

Look at your big

Fat fat bottamus.

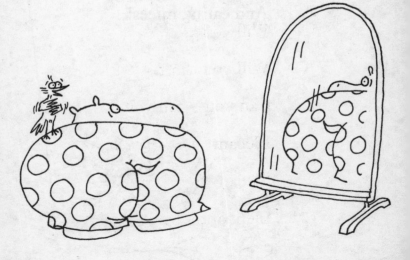

Elephant

Elephant elephant

Will you

Will you can't

Can you – can you

Elecant

Elecan

Elephant.

BOOOOOOOO...!

Owl

The owl at night

Without a light

His eyes can give you

Quite a fright.

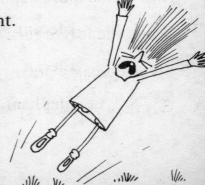

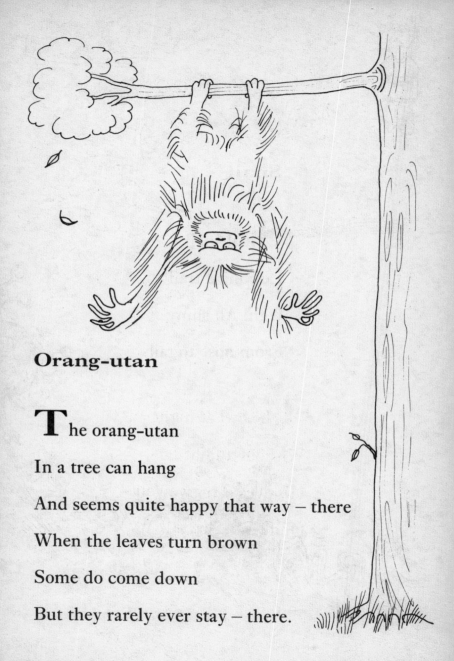

Orang-utan

The orang-utan

In a tree can hang

And seems quite happy that way — there

When the leaves turn brown

Some do come down

But they rarely ever stay — there.

Snail

Snail snail

Leaving a trail

Ugh! All slimy

From nose to tail.

Frog

Frog frog

Jumping frog

He loves to live in

Swamp or bog

And whenever

Whenever he spoke

He went 'croak croak croak'.

CROAK

YOUR HONEY OR YOUR LIFE!

Bee

Busy bee – busy bee

Making lots of honey

And from your work

You silly jerk

Someone else is making money.

Flea

Flea flea

Nipping me

Nipping where

I cannot see

Flea flea

Go away

I'm bitten on

My bum – I say!

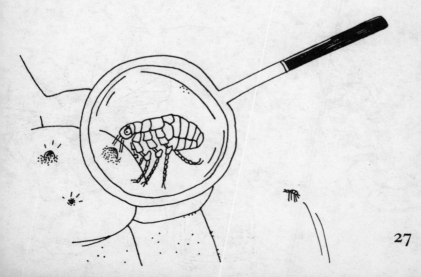

Bug

A bug will bite

Your knees and nose

Nip you everywhere

He goes.

Fly

O fly – little fly

Whizzing whizzing

Whizzing by

Landing on my daddy's nose

On his head on his clothes

Little fly – whizz away

Had enough of you today.

Butterfly

Butterfly butterfly

Making colours in the sky

Red white and blue upon your wings

You are the loveliest of things.

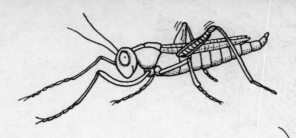

Grasshopper

Grasshopper grasshopper

Making giant hops

In people's gardens

And the farmers' crops

Do be careful where you land

Little green grasshopper

Otherwise you understand

You may come a cropper.

Fish

Fish fish fish fish

In your coat of gold

You will get a lot of money

If you're bought or sold

If you ever sell your coat

Sell your coat of gold

You may get some money

But you'll be very cold.

IT'S
REAL
FISH SKIN,
DEAR!

32

Snake

Slithering slithering

Snake snake

Through the grass

By the lake

Mummy Mummy

Look at him

I never knew

A snake could swim!

33

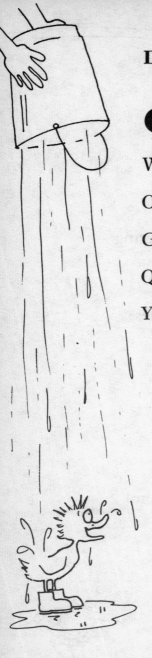

Duck

Quack quack

Water just rolls

Off your back

Going quack quack

Quack quack quackers

You must drive your mummy

crackers!

34

Cockerel

Cock-a-doodle-doo

Goes the cock

Every *every* morning at

Six o'clock

Wakes everybody

Up at dawning

Even on a

Sunday morning.

Cricket

Crick-crick-cricket

Sing your song

Singing singing

All night long

So dear cricket

Now instead

Instead of singing —

Off to bed.

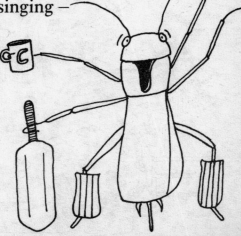

Elephant

Elephant elephant
With your trunk so thin
That is what you use to let
The air get in.

Lamb

Baa-lamb baa-lamb

Crying for your mummy

Time for you to have some milk

From your mummy's tummy.

Chicken

Cluck cluck cluck

That's a chicken

Not a duck

So little hen

Listen to me then

All I beg

Is a nice big egg.

Pig

Pig pig

With your nose

You dig

Digging all

Your dinner out

Dig-dig-digging

With your snout.

CHOCOLATE
TRUFFLES

Leopard

When you see a leopard

You'll see lots of spots

Dot dot dot dot

Dot dot dots!

Tortoise

Tortoise tortoise

Oh so slow

Although you start

You never seem to go.

Gnu

I knew – I knew

It's true – it's true

There's nothing new

About a gnu!

43

Salmon

Salmon salmon

In the River Tweed

You seem to swim

At such a speed

And really salmon

How I wish

You wouldn't end up

On a dish.

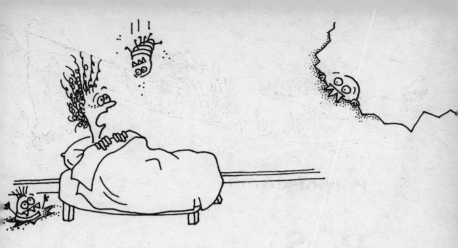

Termite

Termite termite

The hes and shes might

Eat right through your bedroom floor

Eat the window – eat the door

Yet they never stop at that

They'd even eat poor

   Granny's hat!

45

Porpoise

Porpoise you're a clever thing

Swim swim swim swimming

Stay in the sea – the sea is your song

Where you rightfully belong.

Sea-gull

The sea-gull lives by the sea-shore

And what's more

His favourite dish is

Little fishes.

47

Badger

Badger badger

In your set

Wish I had you

As a pet

But I bet

I bet I bet

You're very very

Hard to get.

Piranha

Piranha fishes – piranha fishes

Are very very very vicious

For the moment one dives in

They will strip off all your skin.

March hare

March hare – March hare

Mad as mad can be hare

But do do remember

He's much saner by September.

Whale

Whale whale – right whale

On such a giant scale

It must be lots of fun

To weigh more than a ton.

Moth

Moth moth

Like a piece of velvet cloth

You love the dark of night

But attracted by a light

Sometimes you burn on a candle's

flame

Isn't that an awful shame?

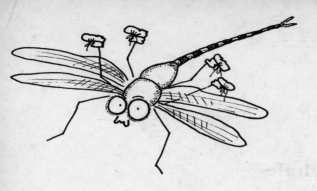

Dragon-fly

Dragon-fly dragon-fly

Flying in the summer sky

Whizzing here – whizzing there

And you keep still in the air!

Whale

Whale whale

The size of your tail

Bring it down with a bash

It does sper–lash.

Wasp

Wasp wasp

With that sting in your tail

If you stuck it in me

I'd send you to jail.

ARREST THAT WASP!

Sea-lion

Sea-lion sea-lion

Playing in the waters

All together mums and dads

And their sons and daughters.

Zebra

Zebra zebra black and white

Oh what a stunning sight

Like pyjamas on the run

Golly gosh what fun what fun.

Antelope

Antelope antelope

Over and over the plains you lope

You have lovely soft brown eyes

Just like Mr Bakewell pies.

Tiger

Tiger tiger such a sight

Through the jungle in the night

Bet you're looking for your lunch

A tasty villager you can munch.

—burp
burrrrp !

BIG
INDIGESTION
TABLETS

Alligator

Alligator alligator
How I hate him – how I hate her
The thought of swimming in your river
Really starts to make me shiver.

Hedgehog

Hedgehog hedgehog

Hedgehog in the garden

Makes snuffling snuffling noise

Please say 'Beg your pardon'.

Fox

Fox fox

Trying to catch a rabbit

Fox fox

What a nasty habit.

Water-buffalo

Water – water-buffalo
Into the water in you go
Wallow wallow wallow wallow
Into every muddy hollow.

Swallow

Swallow swallow

Can I follow

You across the sea

If I did – I pray you bid

Please bring me back for tea.

Sea snake

Sea snake sea snake in the ocean

Swimming with that lovely motion

They say when you reach the shore

You wiggle off to Bangalore.

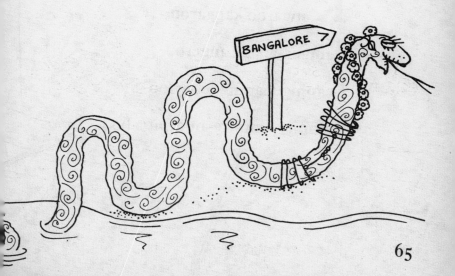

Kangaroo

Kangaroo kangaroo

Lamger–anage angeroo

Leaping leaping leapyloo

Bumpity–umpity–bumpity–boo.

Wart-hog

Wart-hog wart-hog

Are you ever caught hog?

You are very very fat

No there's nothing wrong with that

But lions like you for their dinner

So you'd be much safer thinner.

CAW CAW !

COR!

Crow

The crow – the crow

Is black you know

Caw–caw–caw–cawing

Is very baw–baw–baw–bawring

SNAW
SNAW

Chimpanzee

Chimp-chimp-chimpanzee

Some look like you and some like me

Mr Darwin clearly stated

That some time back we are related.

— MEET DAD!

Toucan

Toucan toucan

You can – toucan

Rattle your beak

But you can't speak.

70

Jellyfish

Jellyfish jellyfish

Like a jelly on a dish

If I covered you with custard

You'd be very very flustered.

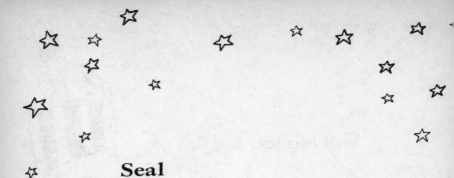

Seal

Seal seal

How does it feel

To swim in icy seas

Thank heavens your blubber

Is thick as rubber

Otherwise you'd freeze.

Ostrich

Ostrich with your skinny legs

Laying laying giant eggs

Never lay one for my tea

I couldn't eat it all you see.

Turtle

Turtle turtle

Heavy shell!

Yet you seem

To swim quite well.

Starfish

Starfish starfish

Lying on the bottom

You like eating little bits

The moment that you spot 'em.

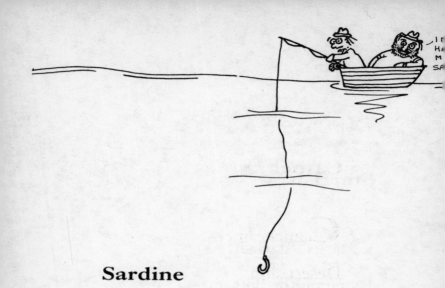

Sardine

Sardine sardine

These days you aren't often seen

The fishermen catch too many

Soon there won't be any.

Camel

Camel camel

Desert ship

You don't need water

On the trip.

Caterpillar

Caterpillar caterpillar

Passing by

Soon you'll be

A butterfly.

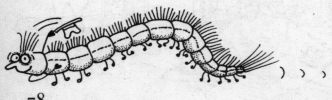

Skate

The skate is flat
Just like a mat
And that my fishy friend
Is that.

NOW WIPE YOUR FISH-FEET!

79

Rhinoceros

The rhinoceros

Is cross with us

'Cause someone's gone

And cut off his horn.

Highland deer

Highland deer – highland deer

I can hear your roars from here

See those antlers oh so grand

Just like my granny's old hat-stand.

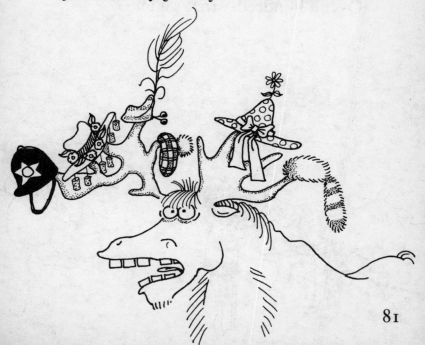

Centipede

Centipede centipede

Over the ground you speed you speed

How many legs then have you got

Over a hundred – that's a lot.

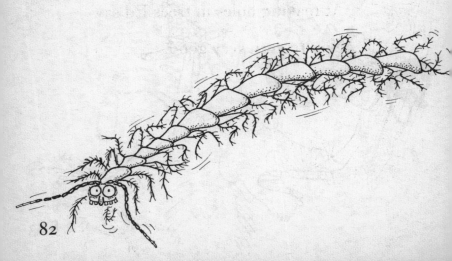

Woodpecker

Woodpecker woodpecker

Pecking at the wood

At making holes in trees I'd say

You're very very good.

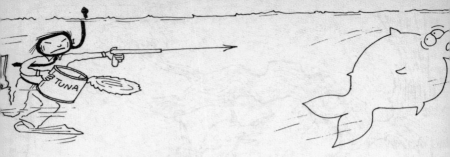

Tuna

Tuna tuna

I know you'd sooner

Not be in a tin

So please please please

You Japanese

Do not commit this sin.

84

HI THERE! I'M
E EARLY BIRD, AND
J'RE
BOUT TO
E A
LATE
WORM!

THAT'S WHAT
YOU THINK!

Worm

Slow worm – slow worm

Never on the go worm

Never never in a hurry

And I don't suppose you worry.

Bluebottle

Bluebottle bluebottle

You're a fly I'd like to throttle

Always landing on my food

Goodness gracious you're so rude!

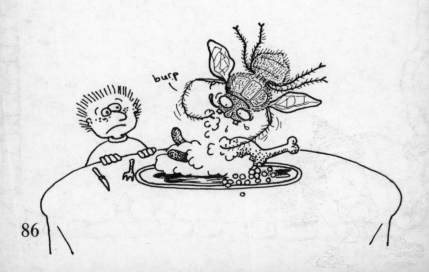

burp

Cockroach

Cockroach cockroach

You're a thing I won't approach

You're supposed to spread disease

As and when and where you please.

Polar bear

Polar bear polar bear

In the Arctic Circle there

You were made a snowy white

So your camouflage is right.

Polecat

Polecat polecat

Whatever made you smell like that

You would really smell quite nice

Using aftershave Old Spice.

Kinkajou

Kinkajou kinkajou

I rarely ever think of you

I don't suppose you think of me

And that is how it's going to be.

Lizard

Lizard lizard

At scurrying you're a wizard

In and out the rocks you go

Like a little dynamo.

Millipede

Millipede millipede

Is very strange you see

He has to use a thousand legs

To get from A to B.

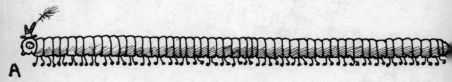

A

Cockatoo

Cockatoo cockatoo

Can I make a friend of you

If you don't want me as a friend

Make your crest stand up on end.

Wolf

Wolf wolf in the snow

Hunting hunting off you go

The finest meal there is for you

Is a nice fat caribou.

Sea-horse

Sea-horse sea-horse

You can't gallop of course

But you have a pair of wings

Sea-horses are the strangest things.

95

Mongoose

M

Mongoose mongoose

You can frighten snakes

Mongoose – strongoose

Think of the courage it takes.

BOO!

96

Yak

The yak – the yak

Will rarely attack

It's a docile little beast

Will not harm you in the least.

"AKKITY –
YAK

97

Otter

Otter otter in a stream

You've a life of which I dream

Frolicking the livelong day

Living just to fish and play.

Ostrich

Ostrich you're a funny bird

People say you look absurd

Others say you look a mess

With your lack of gracefulness.

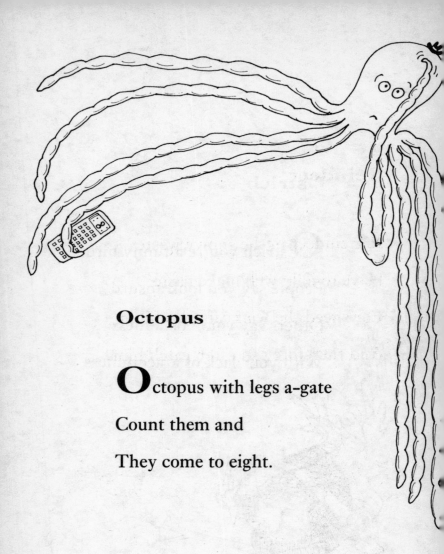

Octopus

Octopus with legs a–gate

Count them and

They come to eight.

Reindeer

Reindeer in the snowy waste

Have to jolly well make haste

For speed the wolf can match him

And therefore can often catch him.

Pretty Polly

Pretty Polly pretty Polly

In the apple tree with your scarlet beak

Eating all the apples up never mind the

squawking

Please save one for me let us hear you

speak!

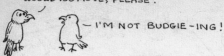

WOULD YOU MOVE, PLEASE?

—I'M NOT BUDGIE-ING!

Budgerigar

Budgerigar budgerigar

What a chatterbox you are

My aunty loves it when

You say, 'Who's a pretty boy, then?'

WHO'S FEELING PRETTY SILLY, THEN?

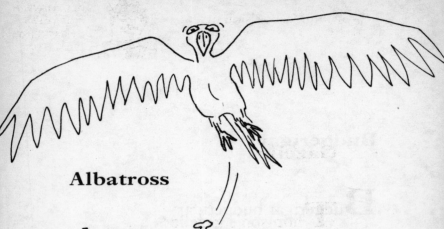

Albatross

Albatross albatross

All the oceans you must cross

Yet you never seem to land

That's something I can't understand.

THE ANCIENT MILLIGAN

I'LL HAVE A TORTOISE NEXT TIME !

Gazelle

Thomson's gazelle

Can run like hell

So though he bought one

He's never caught one.

Boar

Boar boar – wild boar

Eating off the forest floor

You grunt and grunt when you eat food

My mummy says that's very rude.

Lobster

Lobster lobster in the sea

Locked up in your armoury

Just like an ancient knight of old

Except you're very very cold.

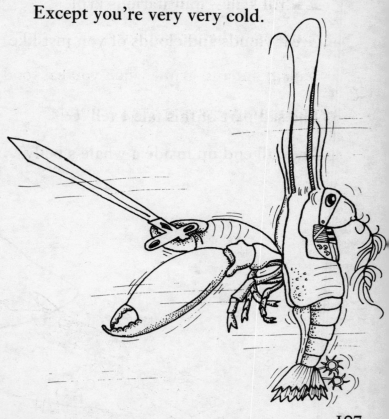

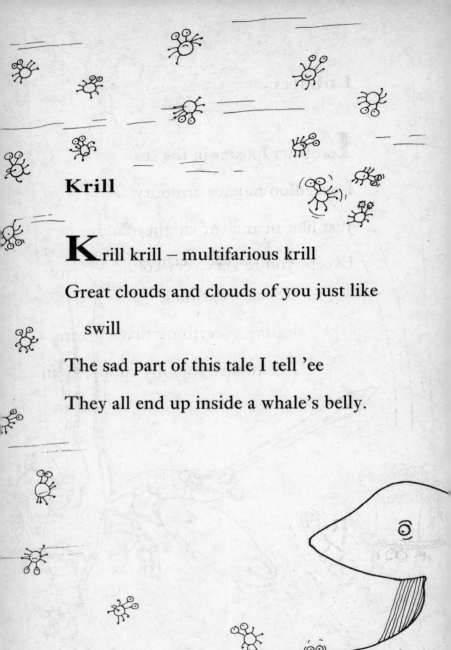

Krill

Krill krill – multifarious krill

Great clouds and clouds of you just like

  swill

The sad part of this tale I tell 'ee

They all end up inside a whale's belly.

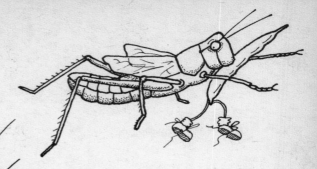

Locust

Hear the warning
Locust swarming
Eating everything that's green
Look there goes my runner bean.

SILLY VERSE FOR KIDS

Here is a collection of more than thirty ridiculous rhymes, all illustrated with Spike Milligan's own absurd drawings, which will amuse and amaze you.

A BOOK OF MILLIGANIMALS

Do you know what a Onecan is? Have you met a Gofongo or the Bald Twit Lion? Can you guess what the Wiggle-Woggle said? Another collection of goonish poems and zany drawings.

UNSPUN SOCKS FROM A CHICKEN'S LAUNDRY

Spike Milligan is of the opinion that children are not just small *homo sapiens* – they are an entirely different species with a secret world that only very perceptive adults have any real knowledge of. He has. Lucky him. Ever since *Silly Verse for Kids* and *A Book of Milliganimals* were first published, children of all ages from nought to four thousand and fifty waited for this further collection of his poems.

STARTLING VERSE FOR ALL THE FAMILY

Whether you're five or five hundred years old, you'll enjoy the irresistible poems that spill out of the pages of this latest collection. A fun book for all the family and everyone else besides.

THE BEST OF FRIENDS
Tony Bradman

A varied and humorous collection of poems which explore just what friendship means to a child. It includes verse from Kit Wright, Colin McNaughton, Roger McGough and many others and looks at many different types of friends in a lively and accessible way.

A MOUSE IN MY ROOF
Richard Edwards

A delicious collection of poetry for younger children which is funny, quirky and highly original. Richard Edwards brings his exceptional and individual wit and charm to an unexpected variety of subjects – even including 'The Thing Extraordinaire'! There are tales with unexpected twists, the strangest of conversations, and a mixture of reality and magic children will love.

SEA IN MY MIND
Selected poems from *The Observer* National
Children's Poetry Competition

This collection of remarkable poetry by children covers a wide range of subjects from love and loss, to people and places, from birds and beasts, to wind and water. Chosen from top entries and award winners in *The Observer* National Children's Poetry Competition, this selection is an enlightening and enjoyable look at the world by young people today.